The BLACKBURN: Dumbarton's Aircraft

by
Alan M Sherry

A Sunderland taking off just opposite Dumbarton Rock, painted by John Stewart Wood.
During the Second World War, John served in the Royal Air Force as a Wireless Operator/Air Gunner.
He was with No. 61 Squadron RAF flying Lancaster Bombers in air operations against the enemy.

ISBN 1 872074 82 0

First Published in the United Kingdom, 1996
By Richard Stenlake Publishing, Ochiltree Sawmill, The Lade, Ochiltree, Ayrshire, KA18 2NX
Phone/fax 01290 423114

Blackburn Bothas under construction, 29 June 1939. *Photograph reproduced by permission of British Aerospace (Defence) Ltd (Brough Heritage Group).*

Acknowledgements

My sincere thanks are due to the many people who helped me in the preparation of this book. As well over a hundred folk were involved these acknowledgements are not exhaustive, but particular thanks are due to the following people:

The Editor, *Aircraft Illustrated*; Barbara Barnes, daughter of the late Ernest Dickens; John Barr of South Lanarkshire Libraries; British Aerospace (Defence) Ltd; The Brough Heritage Group, especially Steve Gillard and his colleagues; Graham Denny, son of the late Sir Maurice Denny; the Fleet Air Arm Museum; The Editor, *Flight International*; Bill Gunston; Elizabeth Henderson, daughter of the late Major Bumpus; Graham Hopner of West Dunbartonshire Libraries and his colleagues;

The Editor, *Hull Daily Mail*; The Editor, Ian Allan Ltd; The Editor, Key Publishing Ltd; The Editor, *The Lennox Herald*; Niall MacNeill of Denny Tank (Scottish Maritime Museum); the staff of West Dunbartonshire Community Education Service; The Editor, Patrick Stephens Ltd; the Public Records Office; The Editor, Putnams; the Royal Aeronautical Society; the Royal Air Force Records Office; the University of Glasgow Business and Commercial Archives; David Vernal of Claremont High School; and Richard Weeks, son of the late Fred Weeks. Many ex-Blackburn workers have loaned me photographs, documents, personal souvenirs and other treasured mementoes. In particular, Barney Coleman; Alastair Crichton; Fergus Steele and Bill Steven have been most helpful.

Dedication

This book is dedicated to Sir Maurice Denny and Mr Robert Blackburn; to former Blackburn workers; and to the memory of Flt/Lt Harry Bailey, Mr Duncan Robertson, and Mr Samuel McMillan, who courageously gave their lives on 7 April 1940, flying in the experimental aircraft, the Blackburn B20.

Contents

Botha in flight, 1939. *Photograph reproduced by permission of British Aerospace (Defence) Ltd (Brough Heritage Group).*

Preface

In the early 1940s, when I was a member of the Air Defence Cadet Corps, I visited the Blackburn Aircraft Company's factory in Dumbarton. I was extremely impressed by the excitement and buzz about the place, and many years later decided to undertake the writing of this book, telling the story of Dumbarton and the Blackburn factory.

Initally the factory was used to train staff, who worked on modifications to the Blackburn Shark and carried out preparatory work on the B20. Once the factory was placed on a 'warning for war' footing in June 1939, work on the Botha, which was already being built at the Brough factory, began in Dumbarton. The first machine rolled off the production line four months later. Between October 1939 and June 1940, the factory at Dumbarton produced an incredible 200 light/medium bombers. Considering the relative inexperience of the staff and the complexity of the aircraft—each with two engines, turrets, guns, bomb doors and flare chutes—this achievement was quite remarkable. Between the summer of 1940 and autumn 1945, the factory also produced 250 Sunderland flying boats. With a wingspan of 112 feet and a fuselage length of over 85 feet, these aeroplanes were as big as a three storey house, and built to accommodate a crew of ten or eleven people. The Dumbarton factory's war-time production record is second-to-none.

When I retired in 1990 I decided to tackle this project, thinking that it would probably take around six months. However, to my dismay I found that most of the factory's official records had been pulped when it closed in 1961. Initially British Aerospace were unable to help me as their records were in bulk storage, although this difficulty was overcome in the last two years with the setting up of the Brough Heritage Group, who have been of enormous help in filling the gaps and providing me with both data and photographs.

In the course of my research for this book I have interviewed over 100 ex-employees of Blackburn and communicated with people as far away as the United States and Australia. I have tried to record the comments of all contributors faithfully, and I hope that the finished book is an accurate and interesting account of Dumbarton and the Blackburn factory.

Alan M. Sherry, October 1996

'We were only lassies at the time!'

Visitors to the Castlehill Housing estate on the outskirts of Dumbarton might be forgiven for wondering why some of the streets carry English names, such as Blackburn and Sunderland.

The group of primary school children that I asked were unable to tell me about the origin of the names, and the teenagers I spoke to were no more helpful. They listened politely to the question, looked at each other and shook their heads. Eventually the spokesman muttered 'Sorry Mac, nae idea'.

However, a sprightly group of ladies in their mid-sixties to seventies had no doubts at all. 'Blackburn Crescent is named after the Blackburn Aircraft Company and Sunderland Avenue is named after the most famous aeroplane made in the factory during the war', they choroused, almost in unison.

'Come with me' ordered one of the women, seizing me by the arm and marching me up to the top of the hill. Turning to face the River Clyde, she asked 'See the rock?'

I nodded.

'Do you see the shadow of the big building on the left, at the foot of it?'

I nodded again. 'Just', I remarked.

'Well that's the Blackburn.'

'Did any of you work there?', I asked.

'Don't be daft, son' said the eldest of the trio, turning round to wink at me.

'We were only lassies at the time!'

Blackburn Bothas under construction at Dumbarton, 1939. *Photograph reproduced by permission of British Aerospace (Defence) Ltd (Brough Heritage Group).*

The Beginnings

In its review of prospects for the coming year, the *Lennox Herald* of 2 January 1937 began with a flourish, proclaiming '50,041,000 tons of naval and merchant shipping on order for the year 1937. The best year for the Clyde since 1919'. Dumbarton's share of this bonanza was 8 ships with a total tonnage of 14,000. Not a huge order, perhaps, but to a community just emerging from the unemployment horrors of the twenties and thirties, this was really good news.

However, further down the column, the good news for the unemployed got even better. Under the headline

New Industry for Dumbarton.
Manufacture of Aircraft in Operation in Nine Months Time

the article read:

Agreement has been reached between William Denny Brothers, the well-known Dumbarton Shipbuilders and Messrs Blackburn Aircraft of Brough, England, to build a factory at Barge Park, Dumbarton to construct aircraft for use by the expanding Royal Air Force.
The factory will provide much needed employment for the skilled, semi skilled and unskilled workers in the Dumbarton / Vale of Leven area.

The Political Background

At the end of the First World War, Britain's casualties numbered over 750,000, and the paralysing debt that she owed the United States for materials supplied during the war meant that she was effectively broke.

Plunged into post-war economic depression, a succession of short-lived governments were elected during the twenties and thirties. In 1929 the Wall Street crash had a catastrophic effect on the British economy. Many businesses collapsed and about 2,750,000 men were left without work. In effect, this meant that 2,750,000 families lost their bread-winner. Very few married women were in work at the time.

Most other nations found themselves in a similar economic position to Britain in the aftermath of the First World War, and horror at the prospect of further carnage meant that rearmament was not on the agenda. Instead, the League of Nations was entrusted with the role of peace-keeping, while most countries attempted to raise their standard of living and gradually rebuild their economy.

However, in direct breach of international treaties then in force, the Fascist powers of Germany and Italy built up a strong army, navy and air force. The League of Nations was too weak to prevent this rearmament and other countries, including the two main European allies of the First World War, France and Britain, chose to ignore the threat.

In late 1935 and again in 1936, Europe was appalled at the sudden and violent eruption of two wars, one in Spain and one in Abyssinia. The Fascist uprising in Spain rapidly developed into a full scale and bloody civil war. Prior to these disturbances the Pacific area had already been stunned by the bloody Japanese invasion of Manchuria in 1931 and the invasion of mainland China in 1932. With a sudden shock of realisation, the governments of Britain and France started to make plans for rearmament, against a background of resistance both from their political opponents and from the population in general.

A new and terrifying weapon was about to change the world's conception of warfare: a kind of warfare which would affect every man, woman and child, not just merely fighting personnel. That weapon was the aeroplane.

A Sunderland on the factory slipway, probably in 1943. *Photograph reproduced by permission of Mrs J. Meikle.*

The Development of Aircraft

Although some aircraft had been used during the First World War, their activity was largely confined to the battlefield. Nonetheless, the comparatively few raids on London and elsewhere in Britain by Zeppelin airships and Gotha aircraft must have provided a foretaste of the kind of terror that this new weapon could cause. Aircraft were used to the full against the civilian population in the wars of Spain, Abyssinia and China, and one only had to glance at a copy of the weekly magazine *Picture Post* to see the horrors of this.

During a period of around twenty years, the aeroplane developed incredibly quickly. In 1919, the fastest machines flew at maximum speeds of around 130 mph, at a height ceiling of 18,000 feet and within a range of around 300 miles. Light private aircraft and commercial long distance machines did not really exist. However by the end of 1936, fighters were flying at speeds in excess of 350 mph and could climb to a height of 35,000 feet, although their operational range was still only 400-600 miles. Bombers with a much longer range could almost match these high levels of performance.

By 1936 prototypes of all the principal combatants in the Battle of Britain—the Spitfire, Hurricane and Messerschmitt Bf109—had all flown. The Messerschmitt was about to enter full production and, later in 1937, would be tested in combat in Spain. On the other hand, the initial contract for the production of 600 Hawker Hurricanes was only awarded in June 1936, while production of the Spitfire was not authorised until later in 1937.

Similar improvements in the field of light and commercial aviation, mainly brought about by the courage and vision of a group of aviation pioneers, were concurrent with the development of military aircraft. The pioneers came from almost every nation in the world, but those best known in this country were perhaps Alcock and Brown, Amy Johnson and Jim Mollinson, Amelia Earheart, and Charles Lindbergh. The small number of private flying clubs that were set up in Britain had very limited membership because of the cost involved. However, the determined band of part-time aviators who joined them later became the backbone of the Auxiliary Air Force, which served the nation so well during the Battle of Britain in 1940. George Pinkerton and Archie McKellar, the famous duo from No. 602 (City of Glasgow) Squadron of the Royal Auxiliary Air Force, were among the early aviators who served their country.

Before the Second World War regular air services within the British Isles and to Europe had also been established. For an affluent few, flights to a distant Empire covering distances in excess of 10,000 miles at a cruising speed of just below 200 mph were also becoming available. But air travel was still a distant dream for the majority of people. At best it involved a five minute 'flip' in an aeroplane during one of Sir Alan Cobham's *National Aviation Day Campaign* tours.

Establishing the Dumbarton Factory

With the increasing likelihood of war during the late 1930s, the Air Ministry began to make provisions for new armament factories. Aware that facilities in the South of England and the Midlands would be within easy reach of the existing German bomber force, a series of so-called 'shadow factories', dispersed in the North of England, Wales and Northern Ireland were already being built. The establishment of a new factory in Scotland was a logical extension to this plan.

Clydeside was well suited to the needs of an aircraft factory, having a local workforce with both engineering and construction skills. There was also a substantial pool of unemployed labour with a broad engineering background, quickly able to adapt to the new skills required for work in the aircraft industry. Furthermore, Dumbarton was well placed to attract a substantial number of workers without depleting the main shipyards in the Greater Glasgow area.

However, probably the most important factor in the decision to locate the factory at Dumbarton was the interest and influence of Sir Maurice Denny, Managing Director of Dumbarton shipbuilders Denny Brothers. For some time Denny had been keen to acquire an interest in the developing aircraft industry, and along with a number of other Scottish industrialists helped establish the Scottish Flying Club at Renfrew Airport in 1927.

In common with most people of his generation, Denny imagined that the Empire would continue to thrive, and predicted that the future for international travel lay in seaplanes and flying boats. In the mid-thirties there were few long distance landplanes. By contrast, Short C Class Empire flying boats had been successfully developed, while huge Boeing Clipper flying boats were already covering the vast tracts of the Pacific Ocean. Denny realised that at some stage in the future aircraft could seriously challenge ships as a means of transporting passengers and freight, thereby threatening his family's interests. With this in mind, he considered setting up a 'seadrome', providing flying boat services between Scotland, Europe, the United States and parts of the Empire, and also proposed plans to build a factory producing flying boats under licence.

Although primarily associated with shipbuilding, Denny Brothers already had links with aviation that were almost as old as the Blackburn Aircraft Company (with whom Denny's subsequently co-operated). In 1910 the Dumbarton company built one of the world's first helicopters. Trials resulted in a successful flight, but the design was not developed, largely because of the onset of hostilities in 1914. Denny Bros had also built 150 BE2e training and reconnaissance aircraft for the Royal Flying Corps during the First World War.

Realising the limitations of his knowledge in this new field, Maurice Denny sought experts to counsel him. His business correspondence, now held by the University of Glasgow, reveals countless correspondences and interviews with both acknowledged and self-professed aviation experts.

Via the Air Ministry, Denny was eventually introduced to Mr Robert Blackburn, founder and managing director of the Blackburn Aeroplane and Motor Company of Brough, Yorkshire. The Blackburn company held a number of contracts for the developing Royal Air Force and the Fleet Air Arm of the Royal Navy, as well as contracts with several foreign governments. Robert Blackburn knew that the company's existing works in Brough and Leeds could not possibly cope with the orders likely to be forthcoming from the rapidly expanding RAF and Fleet Air Arm. A contract for the modification of Blackburn Sharks, then in service with the Royal Navy, had already been awarded. At the same time, the design of the new light/medium bomber, the Blackburn Botha, had advanced to prototype stage, and the award of a sizeable contract appeared to be imminent. The new dive-bomber, the Skua, was at an advanced stage of design and likely to be accepted too, while the problem of where to build the experimental flying boat, the B20, was still to be decided.

The business partnership between Sir Maurice Denny and Mr Robert Blackburn—which also developed into a close personal friendship—consequently came at a very fortunate time. Blackburn was seeking to expand his company's production capacity, while Denny had been looking for an opportunity to enter the field of aviation for some considerable time. Once Blackburn saw the Barge Park site in Dumbarton, the die was cast. Not only was the location perfect for mass-producing the Botha, but it was potentially ideal for building the B20 too.

At first it was uncertain which particular aircraft would be built at Dumbarton. The initial intention was to transfer the contract for the upgrading and maintenance of the Shark, a torpedo/spotter/reconnaissance biplane. However, it was hoped that the experimental, highly secret and revolutionary flying boat, the B20, would also be built there. At a future date the Botha, which had been ordered by the Air Ministry straight from the drawing board, would also be produced at Dumbarton.

With its proximity to water, the site at Barge Park was ideal for the Shark modification programme and B20 production. However, as far as building and delivering landplanes was concerned, its distance from an airport proved an initial problem. Thought was given to adapting the fields at Cardross, where the BE2e was tested and flown from during the 1914-1918 war, but they did not have sufficient length to accommodate modern aeroplanes. This difficulty was solved by transporting the completed machines by ship from Dumbarton to the nearest airfield, Abbotsinch, on the outskirts of Paisley. In his letter to Robert Blackburn of 20 October 1936, Sir Maurice appears to finalise the solution, writing:

transport of the completed machine ex-wings by road is, I think, impossible, but transport by water—one of my original suggestions—appears not only feasible but comparatively cheap and easy.

In the same letter, Maurice Denny confirms his agreement to the establishment of a new company, which would be owned by the two parties, although not in equal measure.

So it was agreed that the factory would be built at Dumbarton, with landplanes produced there transported by a barge, designed and constructed by Denny's. This would be able to transport one aircraft at a time to Abbotsinch, and as a tribute to both companies would be named *Dumbrough*. The barge was built with an open deckhouse, but in deference to the frequently inclement weather on the Clyde, Blackburn workers subsequently constructed an enclosed wheelhouse.

Opposite: Robert Blackburn's first aeroplane, 1908.
Photograph reproduced by permission of British Aerospace (Defence) Ltd (Brough Heritage Group).

The Early Years and The Hartfield Training Depot

Once the broad decision to proceed with the factory at Dumbarton had been made, the pieces began to click into place. Transfer of the ground at Barge Park to the new company was completed in November 1937, and a manager was appointed to oversee the building of the new works and manage them when they commenced production. This man was Major Frank A. Bumpus, who was also Chief Engineer of the new company. Key workers were recruited, selected and appointed, including the designers of the new aircraft and those who would teach the workforce how to build it. No detail was left to chance, or considered too small to examine.

During 1937 the company acquired temporary premises in Dumbarton, allowing training of the new workforce to begin. Production pressures had increased at Brough as the Air Ministry's demands grew, and the contract for the maintenance, modification and repair of the obsolescent Blackburn Shark III, still in service with the Royal Navy at the time, was transferred to Dumbarton. Key workers were brought in from Brough and training at the former Tramway Depot at Hartfield commenced in August 1937.

With rearmament, a shortage of skilled engineers arose, and a two-tier system of payment was introduced at Hartfield in recognition of this.

The Hartfield Training Depot in its former guise as a tram depot, 1907.
Photograph reproduced by permission of West Dunbartonshire Libraries.

Fully qualified engineers, called A-men, were paid more than the trainee B-men they were partnered with. However, many of the so-called engineers did not have a full skill training, while others had not worked at their trade since they had become journeymen. There were teething troubles, as Andrew Stewart recalls.

> Unfortunately, the A-man that I first had to work with had served his time as a plater, but had not worked as [one] since qualifying. He was also quite unable to understand a drawing: he studied the drawings given to him for three or four days without actually doing anything.

However, another B-man, Steve Davis, had quite a different opinion of his partner, Hugh Edwards.

> Hugh, because of his skilled training, was made an A-man, while I was designated as his B-man. We took to each other right away and I was pleased that he really knew what he was doing. It made life so much easier for both of us.

In a subsequent amendment to the scheme, B-men who had acquired the skills of their partners were promoted to 'A' status, a move that was accepted by the whole workforce after objections from some quarters.

Some conflict between the union and the workforce did occur at the new factory. One of the issues raised was the nature of the work carried out by women (who, despite the labels, were members of the A-man/B-man scheme too). To begin with, there was considerable resistance to women operating heavy machinery such as lathes, but due to the shortage of skilled men the union soon relented.

Steve Davis:

> I joined the Hartfield Training Centre in 1937 and became a B-man or semi-skilled operator. I was partnered with a chap called Hugh Edwards. That was the beginning of a long friendship, both at work and in our private lives. I worked on Bothas, Sunderlands, and the Swordfish. Hugh and I worked well together and, even after the cancellation of the A-man/B-man arrangement, we continued to work in the same squad.

Barge Park

Construction of the new factory at Barge Park began early in 1937, and photographs of the site taken in March, April and July that year give an idea of both the scope of the preparation and speed of construction. Operations commenced in late October, when production and modification of the Shark was transferred from Hartfield. However, the training depot was active there for another year, after which it was used for storage. A new machine, the Blackburn Botha, went into production at Barge Park in 1939, and the first completed aircraft rolled off the assembly line four months later in October.

The new Blackburn factory was not just a workplace: with a staff of 4,000, its own fire brigade, ambulance and police forces, and a company of the Home Guard, it bore more resemblance to a small town. As in all communities, friendships were made, many of which became life-long.

Initially, the factory was comprised of three buildings, one of which was a large canteen, which, along with the theatre, became its hub. However, the large 'C' building, housing offices and a wide range of ancillary facilities such as sheet metal shops, a garage and a drawing office, was soon added. Later, a slipway was built with direct access to the river. A siding also connected the factory to the main railway lines.

The Hartfield Depot, 1985. *Photograph reproduced by permission of West Dunbartonshire Libraries.*

The Barge Park factory under construction, 19 March 1937. *Photograph reproduced by permission of British Aerospace (Defence) Ltd (Brough Heritage Group).*

Barge Park under construction, 14 April 1937. *Photograph reproduced by permission of British Aerospace (Defence) Ltd (Brough Heritage Group).*

The Workforce

With the factory completed, the Shark modification programme in full swing, and preliminary work on the secret B20 flying boat underway, the scene was set for a much greater production challenge at Barge Park. By the end of 1938 the Botha prototype had already flown. Although final performance in its four-seat form did not match that expected from the original three-seat design, the Air Ministry realised that it would have to serve as a stop-gap. With the award of the Botha contract consequently imminent, it became clear that a much larger workforce than originally envisaged would need to be recruited.

This came at a difficult time, as there were few skilled and experienced engineers and draughtsmen available. Most Clyde yards had been recruiting experienced personnel in advance of widely expected orders for new war and merchant ships, required under the imminent rearmament programme. As a result, Blackburn spread the recruitment net throughout Scotland, as Andrew Stewart recalls,

> [there were] workers from every town in Scotland and beyond [at the factory]. Of course, there was a big contingent from Dumbarton and the Vale of Leven. Another large group came from Glasgow and Clydebank. I can also recall workmates from Edinburgh, Dundee, Methil, Aberdeen, Buckie, Crossford, Galston, Skye, Wilsontown (the home town of Johnny Scobie) the Isle of Gigha and Islay, as well as a fair number of Englishmen from Brough in Yorkshire. Quite a number of the tradesmen were former shipyard workers such as platers, shipwrights, riveters, riggers and sheet iron workers. There seemed to be a fair number of motor mechanics, engineers, plumbers and various other trades. A motley crew!

Miss Jane Holleran:

> Life wasn't exactly thrilling for a young woman in 1939 and it didn't improve much in the early 1940s. In the main, girls weren't encouraged to think of a career, but were expected to find a suitable husband and settle down to marriage. Blackburn had a lot to offer a girl or young woman: exciting and interesting work in a nice new clean factory, helping the war effort, all at good rates of pay and, of course, lots of young men round about!

> I well remember the day the first Sunderland was launched from the factory. It was quite a sight; it was massive and it dwarfed the hundreds of workers crowding around. Its tailfin seemed to soar into the sky, bigger than the height of a three-storey tenement. Because it was the first to be launched, the Clyde Navigation Trust had somewhat reluctantly agreed to a take-off from the river, so that the workers could get a chance to see the fruits of their labour. After a bit, the engines started up and finally the machine roared off and bumpily soared into the air. After a little while, the pilot turned the aircraft around and it flew majestically over the Rock and the factory. It was a thrilling sight for us to see a machine, which we had built from scratch with our own hands, fly off to the war. I remember that they gave us all a packet of cigarettes to thank us for our efforts. Big deal, eh!

Mrs Jean Floyd:

> I remember I was really surprised when I saw the size of my first pay packet; it was the most money that I had ever earned. After a few weeks, when the honeymoon period of my training was over, I realised why. My job in the delivery department was painstaking and could be very difficult. Why did I do it? Partly for the money, I suppose, and . . . yes, it was my contribution to the war effort, to help our boys who were fighting. Besides, we had a lot of fun after work.

Mrs Margaret Bashford:

> I came to Blackburn as a B-man in 1940. My maiden name was Chisholm and I had three brothers who also worked in the factory with me: Jimmy, Archie and David.

Opposite: Aerial view of factory, c.1946. *Photograph reproduced by permission of British Aerospace (Defence) Ltd (Brough Heritage Group).*

Mrs R. McDougall:

I worked in the Personnel Department. We were confined to our own office and were not allowed to walk through the factory unless particularly instructed to do so. Our passes were checked every day as we entered the works and security was very tight. We all accepted the restrictions willingly, as we didn't want a Nazi spy to infiltrate the works. The officers from the Air Ministry occupied the office just upstairs from ours and they kept strict tabs on all of us. We teenagers were all scared that if we did something wrong or made a mistake we would be locked up in a prison for the duration of the war.

Miss Grace Kennedy:

In 1940, I started work with the company as a B-man. My sister worked in the factory too. I worked mainly on wings and also in the main assembly shop. Sometimes life got a wee bit hectic, but you just got carried along with the enthusiasm and skill of the other workers. They were a pretty good crowd. Did I like my work at the Blackburn ? Like it . . . honestly, I really loved it!

Mrs Anne Harden:

Not long after the outbreak of war in 1939 I was declared redundant from Singers at Clydebank. I went to the unemployment exchange bureau, ('the buroo'), and they gave me an Essential Works Order directing me to report to the Blackburn factory. After interview, I was given a job in the stores in 'D' Building, first of all issuing working drawings, then test plates for metal stress. Later I worked as a progress worker on bomb door assembly.

The Boat Design Office football team, 1937. *Photograph reproduced by permission of Ken McGregor.*

Progress chasers at the factory. From left to right Marie Verbetski, Mrs Jean Graham (nee Gallagher), the late Mrs Margaret Steven (nee Adam). *Photograph reproduced by permission of Bill Steven.*

Mrs Jean Malcolm:

After I left school, I got a job at Denny's Shipyard as a 'Catch Girl', catching rivets and placing them for the riveter to batter into the plates that made up the ship. The only snag was that they were red hot at the time and also I was standing on a plank about a mile above the ground. I had to work out of doors in all kinds of dreadful weather, but it wasn't too bad a job. Nonetheless, it was quite a difference when I came to the Blackburn to work indoors in nice clean conditions, with most of my workmates in the section being women. What a laugh we had!

Mrs Sarah McFall:

Discipline in the factory was very strict with severe penalties for missing a day away from work. The only acceptable reason for absence was illness and this required a doctor's certificate. I remember a man in my section took an afternoon off to go to the pictures and he was questioned about this absence the next day. He was unable to produce a valid reason for his absence and was fined heavily. I think that he was fined a whole week's wages with the warning that a further offence would lead to imprisonment.

Jessie McNicol:

I worked in the Blackburn from 1942 until 1945. I spent most of my time fitting stringers to the wings before they were plated with metal sheeting. The work was sometimes exhausting, but I felt as if I had done my bit for the war effort and helped our boys to win.

Mrs Mary McGinlay:

I was a riveter in the factory. All the work was interesting, but there was always pressure. Pressure that you made yourself in trying to beat the rate fixer as well as pressure from management to work more efficiently. That doesn't mean that I didn't enjoy my work or feel proud of it. Of course I did! Brandishing my Desouter Rivet Gun and armed with my newly acquired skill, I can tell you I felt on top of the world. I was in the factory from 1940 till 1943 and my 'holder-on' was Tilly Allison. I'm still friends with her today.

Mrs Dolly Thomson:

In 1940, I was working for the Aeronautical Inspection Directorate at Thorntonhall near East Kilbride. Four of us girls provided a secretarial service for the members of the Inspectorate throughout Scotland. The Blackburn Botha was the only complete aircraft being manufactured in Scotland at that time and because it was relatively small there was no need for a constant presence at the site. Suddenly, all that changed and we were asked to volunteer for transfer to the Blackburn factory at Dumbarton. The work with the inspectorate at Blackburn was extremely pressured and we had to work like billy-o and sometimes like billy-o plus. Being both young and single, my time at Blackburn was much enjoyed and nice to look back on.

Mrs Madge Kane:

I joined Blackburn in 1940. Nowadays it all seems so unlikely, but I was made a riveter and worked mainly on the fuselages of the Sunderlands. It was a really big machine and sometimes you had to crawl under the step and inside the fuselage. It could be quite scary. I remember the laughs, the friendships, the hard work, being tired and perhaps mainly those uncomfortable rides in Bailey's buses.

Jenny Mitchell:

I joined Blackburn and was trained as a riveter. After training I got what seemed a massive wage, but I soon found out the reason for getting that sort of money.

Robert Haig:

I joined the factory in 1937 and to begin with I worked in the old tramway sheds at Hartfield, fitting the floats to Blackburn Sharks. I was fifteen years with Blackburn and during that time I worked on Sharks, Bothas and of course Sunderlands. Latterly, I was mostly involved in inspection work, to ensure that the quality of workmanship was maintained. I had some good times in the factory and some difficult ones too. If you ask me to pick out the thing that still lurks in my memory, I suppose the incident involving Captain 'Blood' stands out clearly in my mind. The very first

Timekeepers at the Dumbarton factory, 1942. *Photograph reproduced by permission of West Dunbartonshire Libraries.*

Sunderland was flown from the factory, but after that, the aircraft were towed from Dumbarton down river to the Marine Aircraft Experimental Establishment at Rhu on the Gareloch. This was because the Clyde Navigation Trust feared that the walls of the Clyde's main navigation channel would be damaged by the wash from high speed taxiing. The tow was tedious, took a long time and in bad weather was simply not possible. This practice continued for some time until a new test pilot arrived: his name was Group-Captain Flood. Initially, he asked to be taken for a short trip in a launch along Blackburn's private channel to the point just before it reached the main channel of the river. Everybody thought that he was scared of taxiing in the confined waters of the river. You can imagine the surprise of the workers, when he started the engines on the slipway and allowed then to warm up fully. Next, when he reached the bottom of the slipway, he slammed the throttles open and taxied at high speed down the private channel, becoming airborne just as the main river channel was reached. Managers and workers gasped as the aircraft banked down river toward Greenock, avoiding the Langbank Hills which stood directly in the flight path. The workers, who were certain that his action would lead to him coming to a sticky end, began to refer to him as Captain Blood. After this experimental fly-off, all Sunderlands were flown directly to the MAEE at Rhu.

Fergus Steele:

I joined the Blackburn workforce as an aero engineer in 1937. As well as working on the Shark, I recall carrying out repairs on an a handful of Skua's, the Royal Navy's latest dive-bomber, and on one Roc aircraft (the fighter version of the Skua, which, like the pioneering Boulton-Paul Defiant had a four-gun power driven gun turret). I also remember repair work being carried out on the tail fin of the B20, when, following initial test flights in 1940, it was struck by birds just prior to its official test programme.

Wartime secrecy shrouded all events in the factory, and the fire on the Botha construction line was never revealed in the press. It happened on a Saturday morning in May 1940 when, together with an young apprentice, I was working in the finishing shop and the Botha was standing over an inspection pit. The pit was packed with finishing felt and the machine's tailwheel was resting on the weighbridge. Work was in progress on snagging and fitting deadening felt within the aircraft. At the same time, flow tests on the fuel system were taking place just beyond the weighbridge and fumes permeated the whole workspace. The felt lining was fixed to the metal skin of the aircraft using two different kinds of Bostik: one in a yellow tin and the other in a black tin. Separately, the two ingredients were harmless, although together they were highly inflammable. As the apprentice worked along the narrow confines of the aircraft, he accidentally tipped the contents of one tin into the other, and the workspace burst into flames, quickly enveloping him. I was working a little further down the aircraft. I grabbed the boy, rolled him on the ground and succeeded in putting out the flames. The fire on the Botha was quickly contained by other workers and did not spread to other areas of the factory. The subsequent enquiry made recommendations for the future separation of the two processes.

Alfred Gibb:

As an aircraft fitter, my main job was building the frames for the mainplanes. It was difficult, exacting and painstaking work, but I found it interesting and absorbing.

Ken McGregor:

I joined Blackburn in 1937 as an Apprentice Draughtsman in the Flying Boat Design Office. The main work of the office was the detailed planning of the experimental Flying Boat, the Blackburn B20. The machine was constructed in the Final Assembly Shop under conditions of extreme secrecy, with many of the personnel on special release from the Royal Air Force.

Andrew Stewart:

I joined Blackburn in September 1939 as a B-man. After a very brief period of training in the Hartfield depot, I was sent along to the main works, initially to the fuselage construction section where I worked on the new Botha. I was later transferred to work on the Short Sunderland. Having become a fairly skilled worker, I found the new task of fitting the flying controls to the Sunderland most interesting. Initially, it seemed a very long and dangerous journey along the fuselage, especially as the slightest slip could have meant a fall to the hard concrete floor twenty feet below. But like everything else we got used to it and soon we were running along the top of the fuselage without a thought. Eventually, we got rather clever and rigged up a telephone which saved a great deal of movement.

Malcolm Wallace:

In a busy work place, like the Blackburn factory, it was difficult to avoid cuts and bruises, and despite being a haemophiliac, I worked on all sections of the B20 at Dumbarton. I vividly remember the shock on hearing of the fate of the machine on its trials in 1940.

Alastair W. Crichton:

I have vivid memories of the group of Norwegian seaplanes which arrived at the factory around the end of April 1940 for repair and modification. I remember being shattered to see that they were riddled with machine gun bullets. The stress tests on the B20 are another clear memory. They were carried out in front of the factory, the machine being secured by giant concrete blocks. Each engine was then run up in turn, and the stress on the various components measured. The B20 crash devastated us all quite beyond description and there was an immediate summons for all design and construction heads of departments who were working on the B20 to go down to Brough.

Hugh Galloway:

There was quite a security rigmarole surrounding work on the B20, and a special pass was required to gain access to that part of the building. I was a riveter and my job was to rivet the hull plates on the fuselage, with quite a lot of work on the step. Flt Lt Bailey, complete with his usual uniform of bowler hat and raincoat, visited us fairly regularly, and I think that he was anxious to fly the machine. Freddy Weeks, one of the two survivors of the crash, worked in the B20 team and I thought a lot of him.

Robert Donald:

I started work at the Blackburn when I left school in 1940. I was fourteen at the time, and worked as an office boy until I could begin an apprenticeship. I left the factory in 1944 when I was

called up to serve in the mines. By that stage of the war, not all conscripts were sent to the armed services, but an increasing number were drafted to occupations which had a shortage of labour. The decision was made by ballot and the individual had no say in the matter.

Bill Steven:

I worked on Sunderlands in the detail fitting shop, fitting wings, engines, fuel systems and hydraulics. I worked in Dumbarton until 1944, when I was transferred to the modification unit at Abbotsinch (now Glasgow Airport) My job was to carry out modifications to aircraft such as Hellcats and Corsairs. I spent many happy years at Blackburn before retiring.

Jack Sloss:

I enjoyed the detailed nature of my work as a cost clerk. Material and labour costs were strictly controlled and had to square and meet the target figure. It was particularly demanding work, but most satisfying when your figures added up. I costed all of the aircraft built at the works, largely because closely controlled costing was my specialism. The war-time years were stressful; I could often see figures in my mind's eye as I fell asleep, indeed sometimes I would wake in a cold sweat, wondering if I had made an error, and could hardly contain myself until the next day to get into the office to double check the figures. All in all, I really enjoyed my work at the factory and made many friends there.

Gordon Wright. Mrs Barbara Wright, Gordon's widow recalls:

Gordon was a plater and worked on the B20 from 1939. He was a fine man and enjoyed his work on the B20 and also later work on the Sunderland. When the B20 crashed in 1940, he was devastated like all the other folk who worked on the machine. Flt/Lt Bailey, Freddy Weeks (one of the two survivors) and two other co-workers called Robertson and McMillan were always speaking to the construction crew and asking about this and that, so they were personal friends.

Opposite: The Blackburn factory Home Guard, 1941.
Photograph reproduced by permission of Hugh Edwards.

Raiding the Royal Air Force

By the end of 1941, the dire shortage of skilled engineers was beginning to seriously affect production. Aircraft were becoming much more complex, and the need for a greater skill level amongst engineers consequently increased. All aircraft factories were experiencing the same difficulty and, as a result, the government decided that the armed forces should be trawled for suitable candidates. Notices began to appear at RAF stations throughout Britain asking for suitably qualified volunteers to serve in aircraft factories in Britain, Canada and the United States (where there were also shortages). A number of airmen, particularly those involved in training units, responded. Bernard (Barney) Coleman, a Leading Aircraftsman Flight Mechanic, working at a Bomber Command Operational Training Unit (OTU), was a typical example.

> Prior to the outbreak of war, I was a motor mechanic and had already volunteered for service with the Royal Air Force Volunteer Reserve. Because of the rush of volunteers, my service was deferred and, following the Direction of Labour Act, I was sent to work in the aircraft industry. I was finally called up in early 1941 and, after training, was posted to carry out servicing and maintenance of heavy bombers in an OTU of Bomber Command. One day I saw an advertisement asking for qualified volunteers to serve on attachment to aircraft factories in the United States, Canada and the United Kingdom. As I quite fancied being posted to Canada or the USA, or even close to my home town in Norfolk, I applied. Eventually in May 1942, I heard that my application had been approved and that I was to be posted to Dumbarton. I hadn't a clue where Dumbarton was: some of my mates said that it was in the United States, but I soon met a Jock airman who quickly corrected that error. I had never been in Scotland before and it was with some trepidation that I arrived at the hostel in Balloch. It was clean and comfortable, but it meant the usual service business of queuing for meals
>
> As production rose and factory personnel became properly trained, the RAF began to request the return of servicemen as it was also being hit by a skills shortage, caused both by casualties and the increase in the number of aircraft flying. I was eventually recalled to the Air Force in July 1943 and posted to 56 Maintenance Unit at RAF Longmains near Inverness. The work at the unit was mainly aircraft recovery and salvage; a difficult and demanding task. We were equipped with three ton trucks and lived a nomadic existence, travelling throughout the remote areas of the Scottish Highlands, with hours and sometimes days spent at crash sites, often on remote hillsides, glens or deserted coastal areas. The aircraft were mostly from Operational Training Units, or were returning from operations with casualties aboard. Our job began after the removal of the dead and injured aircrew and our main task was to recover parts and equipment for repair and re-use. We struggled through peat bogs and up and down hills, using giant metal sledges to recover the valuable material. In the course of my service with the unit I came across at least two Sunderlands that I had worked on during my time in the factory, but fortunately their demise had not been caused by any lack of attention to detail on my part; but rather by adverse weather conditions, or having suffered during operations against the enemy. The work was both arduous and tiring. What a change from my work with Bothas and Sunderlands in the comfortable, heated factory in Dumbarton.

Air Raids

Until 13 March 1941, the Clyde had been relatively free of major air raids. However, just as the sky began to darken that evening, barrage balloons started to climb into the sky in Glasgow and in other towns in the West of Scotland—a sure sign that enemy activity was about to start. Later on, the asymmetrical beat of aircraft engines, said to be a trademark of enemy aircraft, began to be heard. This was followed soon after by the crump of bombs and the sharper crack of the anti-aircraft fire from ships on the Clyde. More air raids hit the area the following night.

A comparatively small number of bombs were destined to fall on Glasgow that night, and it soon became clear that the target lay somewhere further to the west. That target was Clydebank and its shipyards, and much of the town was almost destroyed that night.

However, as well as Clydebank, the two nearby sites of Denny Brothers' yard and the Blackburn Aircraft factory, just a few miles away in Dumbarton, were also clearly identified on Luftwaffe war maps. Blackburn was not seriously bombed that night, although the scale of the attack on Clydebank caused quite a scare. The Clyde shipyards had been in dispute over pay and a major apprentices strike was in process at the time. However, in the light of this new threat almost everyone reported for duty the following morning.

Dumbarton's turn was to come on the evenings of 5 and 6 May 1941. The principal thrust of the Luftwaffe's attack was on shipyards and shipping around Greenock and Port Glasgow, although attacks on Denny's yard, the Blackburn factory and ships in and around the Leven estuary were also made that night using high explosive bombs—so-called land mines—as well as incendiaries. Three of the high explosive devices landed on the Blackburn factory. Says Andrew Stewart,

> when we entered the factory, the land mine could be seen hanging by its harness from the parachute, which was caught in the roof of the Final Assembly hall. The workforce was sent home and the factory closed for the day until the bomb disposal experts could

defuse the weapon. We were thunderstruck to learn later that some character had volunteered to defuse it himself: fortunately he was dissuaded from his task. There is little doubt that, had the mine exploded, the factory would have been destroyed, or at the very least badly damaged.

Malcolm Wallace remembered that there were further repercussions from this incident: the worker was charged with endangering the factory by interfering with an enemy explosive device, and received a term of imprisonment. Alastair Crichton had other recollections of that night, which are not possible to substantiate from official records.

> I remember that there were two different types of air raid shelters: one type was soft-skinned, the other hard skinned. On May 5/6, the women were directed to the hard one, the men to the other. The latter took a direct hit and a number of men were killed.

Official records show that only three explosive devices were found in the Blackburn factory, and none was shown as being near a shelter or to have caused injury. Was there an official cover-up?

Blackburn Shark with wheels, 1937. *Preceeding page*: A Shark, this time with floats.
Photographs reproduced by permission of British Aerospace (Defence) Ltd (Brough Heritage Group).

'Mods' and Things

Machines as complex as the aircraft built in Dumbarton frequently required modification to equip them for particular tasks and fine-tune their performance. Initially, most manufacturers tried to cope with modifications as the need arose, but as the war advanced most had to set up specialist repair and modification sections. Blackburn was no exception. The Ministry of Aircraft Production was aware how deftly Blackburn had dealt with the problems which affected their own machines, and also how well they had coped with modifications to other manufacturers' aircraft. In the early forties, Britain began to receive aircraft from the USA under the Lend-Lease scheme. This was designed to allow Britain to continue to use American armaments which it could no longer afford to buy. The theory was that Britain would receive the armaments on a lease, with ownership remaining in American hands. Material not destroyed by enemy action would be returned to the USA after the war was over.

The United States had the edge over Britain in the field of carrier-borne aircraft. Machines like the Wildcat (initially used by the Royal Navy and called the Martlet), the Hellcat, the Corsair and the Avenger (initially called the Tarpon) were much more advanced than their British counterparts in terms of performance. However some of their equipment was not so well suited to European climatic conditions as machines that were designed specifically for it, and thus a considerable amount of modification was required to meet the needs of the European theatre.

Because of their experience with carrier-borne aircraft, Blackburn were asked to establish repair and modification centres to deal with these problems. Three were set up around Brough and three in Scotland near Dumbarton—at Prestwick Airport, at Abbotsinch Airport and in Renfrew in Ogston and Tenant's former soap works. Around 4,000 modifications and repairs were carried out by the Dumbarton controlled units. As Bill Steven recalls,

I worked at Abbotsinch and the work was not easy. For my part I was involved with bringing the electrical, radio and radar systems up to date and this was a complicated task. The work also included making the radio and intercom systems compatible with British systems. The American machines were beautifully finished, but their equipment was often affected by our weather conditions.

Fergus Steele at Hartfield with Shark, 1937.
Photograph reproduced by permission of Fergus Steele.

... Apart from work

At one stage 4,000 people worked at the Blackburn factory, and the social life that developed around it was as important as the work itself.

The great West of Scotland passion of "the dancin'", or "the jiggin'", was incredibly popular during the thirties and forties. Every night, Monday to Saturday, thousands of young people danced together in crowded ballrooms. There were no disc jockeys, and although one or two tennis clubs and the like had private dances with records, most people enjoyed live bands ranging from three, to fifteen or even twenty piece, playing all the popular hits of the day. Band leaders were cult figures and some dancers swore that the tempo of X Band was more correct than that of Y, and would travel miles just to dance with it. Many devotees declared that Jack Chapman of the Plaza in Glasgow was the best, but others didn't agree. Some made for the main Glasgow dance halls like the Locarno, Plaza, Dennistoun Palais, Barrowland or, for the more sedate, the Albert, but others preferred to stay in their home town of Dumbarton and patronise either the Masonic or Burgh halls.

Along with ballroom dancing, going to the pictures was the most popular form of entertainment in the forties. Most Dumbarton people of that 'certain age' can recall the names of popular cinemas in a flash ... the Rialto, The Regal, the Picture House and the La Scala automatically trip off their lips, as do the names of the big stars of the time such as Clark Gable and Jean Harlow. When I mentioned the pictures, comments came fast and furious, along with many happy memories. This isn't really surprising when one considers that at the time a few pence bought a warm comfortable seat, and the chance to be temporarily transported to a different and much more glamorous world.

Sadie McFall:

It was murder waiting in a queue in the pouring rain before you got in to the cinema, but it was well worth it. You got a chance to see those lucky people in America who all seemed to be as rich as anything, with big cars and houses . . . it was really just like a dream. Great!

Margaret Bashford:

The pictures were my all-time favourite thing to do.

Jean Malcolm:

You thought that the film was reality and your work at Blackburn was the film, if only for a couple of hours.

Grace Kennedy:

I was absolutely crazy about the pictures. Any kind would do, but I would often go to a cinema miles away from Dumbarton, if there was a special picture that I had missed seeing when it was being shown in Dumbarton.

Operation Blackburn Fido and Other Secret Projects

During the 1939-45 war, the Blackburn factory was the scene of many secret activities, but none more so than 'Operation Fido'. Because of the diversion of all sorts of material to the war effort, there was a continuing shortage of nearly everything, and one which deeply affected most families was the acute lack of toys. Aircraft manufacture produced a great deal of scrap material of all kinds, and meal breaks, especially during the Christmas period, were often the scene of frenzied activity as people made a range of different toys. The ingenuity of the workforce was evident in the variety of toys produced, as Andrew Stewart recalls:

Kaleidoscopes were in great demand, as they were easily produced from discarded packing tubes, strips of scrap aluminium, a small piece of mirror and bits of coloured glass—all held together by sticky tape. I suppose that the different shifts of the workforce produced different toys, and some folk preferred to keep their efforts under wraps. It is doubtful, however, if any of these projects were subject to the same level of secrecy as Operation Fido. I remembered that a pal of mine had an old pre-war toy called Fido. It was a walk-along dog and, as there was a great shortage of action or wind-up toys, I asked him if he still had it. He did, although it had two legs missing. Having acquired it I persuaded a friendly joiner to make me two legs identical to those that remained on the toy. Fido consisted of a body made of plywood, with legs attached by thin metal tubing. The secret lay in the camber of the legs, which, when correct, gave a realistic walk when the toy was pulled along by a piece of string. Once workers had seen a demonstration, the demand for the plans of Fido was unbelievable. It was quite a comical sight to see a dozen or so grown men exercise their toys at mealtimes. Many Dumbarton children must have got great pleasure from the Blackburn Fido. Work at Blackburn was not always serious: occasionally, there were some lighter moments!

Fergus Steele working on Shark tail-wheel assembly at Hartfield, 1937. *Photograph reproduced by permission of Fergus Steele.*

The Spitfire on Floats

One of the more common war-time myths that continues to circulate amongst factory employees is the story of the Spitfire on floats. There are several versions in Blackburn folklore, but this is the most popular one:

One late afternoon in mid-April 1940, the barge *Dumbrough*, which had been built to transport the completed Bothas from the factory to Abbotsinch airfield, returned from its daily run. Normally the crew would have expected to have tidied up and gone home at that time, although on this particular day they were asked to return to Abbotsinch to collect a special cargo. This was a brand new Supermarine Spitfire fighter aircraft, which had been specially flown up from the factory at Castle Bromwich and dismantled for transport to Dumbarton. In the fading evening light, the *Dumbrough* ferried the machine down river to the Dumbarton factory, where a team of designers and engineers worked through the night to produce and equip it with a special pair of floats . At first light, it was taken by road to the Marine Aircraft Experimental Establishment at Rhu near Helensburgh, where it was successfully test flown at 7.15 in the morning.

It's a lovely story, it sounds perfectly plausible, but unfortunately it's simply not true. The real version can be found in the definitive book on the Supermarine, *Spitfire, The History*, by Eric B. Morgan and Edward Shacklady (Key Publishing). In April 1940, serious thought was given to equipping the fighter with floats, and Blackburn was amongst those firms selected to design and produce around fifty pairs. The floats, which were normally fitted to the Blackburn Roc, were tried out and proved to be unsuccessful, as did others designed by Blackburn and also Folland Aircraft. Three examples of the machine were experimentally fitted with floats and a Spitfire on floats did finally arrive at the MAEE at Rhu for testing and assessment, but not until 1943. The project was not a success and the idea was abandoned, although one machine was transferred to the Middle East for testing.

The End of the War

Towards the beginning of 1945, it became apparent that the tide of war was turning in favour of the Allies, and that it was only a matter of time before hostilities in Europe would end. The future of the war against Japan in the Far East was an unknown quantity, but peace in Europe was becoming a real possibility.

Much had changed during the war years. Young service men and women had been exposed to a whole new set of experiences, and the government knew that people would expect a much higher standard of living as they returned to civilian life. Along with plans for a National Health Service, mooted by the Beveridge Plan in 1944, housing was considered to be a major issue. Much of Britain's pre-war housing stock was sub-standard, and along with several other firms, Blackburn was invited to tender for the supply of a range of temporary pre-fabricated houses which could be erected quickly and easily on prepared foundations.

In April 1945, Blackburn received a small initial order to supply prefabs to a number of Scottish Local Authorities. The war in Europe ended on 8 May, while hostilities in the Far East ceased dramatically and suddenly following the bombing of Hiroshima and Nagasaki. With the end of the fighting, aircraft contracts were slashed and terminated. Blackburn was not exempt from the cuts, and Sunderland production ceased with the last machine, VB889, being launched on 19 October 1945. In the words of Rose McGregor, 'the work went on, but the buzz was simply not there.'

The production of houses continued not only for the home market but also for export. Many countries had housing shortages and the attraction of easily transported prefabs was obvious. The project was a much greater success than anyone had originally anticipated and the work generated by the production of houses lasted for quite a number of years, as these accounts confirm.

Barney Coleman:

Having been recalled by the RAF in 1944, I returned to Blackburn's Dumbarton factory in August 1946. To begin with there were a few odd jobs on Sunderland parts, modifications and repairs, but these soon dried up and I was moved to the prefab assembly line. In late 1947 I was approached by my former foreman, Jack Boag, one of the original staff from Brough, who asked me to join him in starting an outside and contract maintenance unit for the prefab housing

A convoy of the first houses leaving the factory, 1946. *Photograph reproduced by permission of West Dunbartonshire Libraries.*

stock. We acquired three ex-Navy vans from the ordinance depot at Bishopton and fitted them out as mobile workshops. By January 1948, we were on the road. Each van had a crew of four (a fitter or labourer/driver, a joiner, an electrician and a plumber), although after six months we were all proficient at each others' jobs, and worked as a team without demarcation lines. I had taken advantage of a number of courses on offer prior to my demob, including driving instruction, and also became a part-time instructor, teaching the tradesmen to drive on site. We covered the length and breadth of Scotland and the North of England. When the prefab contracts finished in 1952 we moved on to traditional housing with prefabricated interiors. The last stage in housing for Blackburn was the Terrapin mobile bungalow which was widely used by the services and for overseas government contracts. At the end of my service, I managed to buy one of these excellent buildings, and it's still in use today.

David Thorburn:

I served my apprenticeship at Denny Brothers in Dumbarton and also spent some time at John Brown's in Clydebank. I was always particularly proud that, while at Denny's, I helped to construct the Havoc and the Hasty, two of the fastest destroyers in the Royal Navy. In 1946, I transferred to the Blackburn and worked on the first fifty prefab houses. The showhouse was in Smollet Road and the houses we built were erected at Silverton High Mains. Blackburn was a good employer and the factory was quite a nice place to work.

Barney Coleman with one of the mobile prefab maintenance units, 1947. *Photograph reproduced by permission of Barney Coleman.*

A Sunderland on the factory slipway, c.1943. *Photograph reproduced by permission of Mrs J. Meikle.*

Aircraft Production at Dumbarton in the Post-War Years

When the last Sunderland, VB889, was completed on 25 October 1945 and successfully test flown on 8 November 1945, the management and workforce were in buoyant mood. After all, who could blame them. Their record of building aircraft to a high standard, to contract price, and to deadline was second to none. They also had a unique skill in the production of flying boats. The war had proved beyond all doubt—almost exactly in line with Sir Maurice Denny's prophetic view and Robert Blackburn's vision of the future—that aircraft would be the people-carrriers of the future. They also had supreme confidence in the product that they had produced, and rightly so; the VB889 took part in the Berlin Airlift and was still flying in 1954.

To capitalise on the experience gained in building this aircraft, Major Rennie (the company's Chief Seaplane Designer) had undertaken a design study for a civilian flying boat, and a model was built at the Dumbarton factory. The flying boat B49 was to be called *The Clydesman* as a tribute to the Dumbarton workforce. In *Blackburn Aircraft since 1909*, published by Putnam, the late A.J. Jackson writes:

> . . . the design was for a high wing all-metal monoplane 202 feet in span and 148 feet long overall, with a hull and tail unit of similar outline to the Sunderland flying boats which the firm built on the Clyde during the war. With an all up weight of 138 tons and cruising at 270 mph at 15,000 feet, its range with 160 passengers and 30,400 lbs of freight and mail would have been 2,500 miles. Alternatively, with 72 passengers and 2,980 lbs of freight and mail the range was 4,375 miles. Sleeping accommodation was provided in a pressurised cabin with two decks and there were full galley and dressing room facilities. Maximum speed 307 mph, initial climb 940 ft/min, absolute ceiling 20,000ft.

A victim of time, speed, the jet engine and the move toward landplanes,

the B49 was never built, and in the event the model was the last complete aircraft built at Dumbarton. It's true that after 1945 parts and components were constructed in the factory, but most of them were not intended for use in aircraft designed by Blackburn.

However, the design team at Blackburn were certainly not idle, and between 1945 and 1961 they produced 73 different designs for civil and military aircraft. Only three of these designs were actually built in any quantity, the Firebrand, Beverley and Buccaneer. A small number of others were built as mock-ups and prototypes, but were never developed. None of the three machines selected for production were wholly produced at Dumbarton, although parts for the Beverley and the Buccaneer were certainly manufactured there. It is amazing to think that Buccaneers flew operationally in the Gulf War of 1992, more than 30 years after they entered squadron service and almost forty years after Robert Blackburn first announced the Buccaneer contract to the company's Annual General Meeting in August 1955. It speaks volumes for the quality of the machine and Dumbarton workers have every right to feel proud to have contributed to this aircraft in no small measure.

With the completion of the contract for the Buccaneer, aircraft production at Dumbarton finally came to an end. An odd modification and repeat order for replacement parts did find its way there, but very rarely. Thereafter the factory, by now designated Blackburn Engineering Division, was touting hard for business of any kind and orders—generally very small—were accepted for cabin cruisers, dinghies, and trailers amongst other things. The workforce, which had totalled over 4,000 at its war-time peak, dwindled to around 400, with large numbers deserting the obviously sinking ship. In August 1960 the factory closed, although a small number of employees remained in the engineering and office facilities until early in 1961. The watch that Jack Sloss, Chief Cost Clerk, received on his retiral in 1961 bore the inscription 'Blackburn Aircraft, Dumbarton, 1937 to 1961'.

Opposite: The first Sunderland built at Dumbarton nearing completion, 5 August 1941. Photograph reproduced by permission of British Aerospace (Defence) Ltd (Brough Heritage Group).

Hartfield Training Depot, 1937, with work on Blackburn Sharks in progress. The old tram lines are visible in the foreground.
Photograph reproduced by permission of British Aerospace (Defence) Ltd (Brough Heritage Group).

Aircraft Built at the Clyde Factory in Dumbarton, 1937-1945

The Blackburn Shark B6 Mark III

The Blackburn Shark Mark III was the first aircraft allocated to the Training Depot at Hartfield, and was assembled from components produced at the Brough factory. Modifications to upgrade the Shark for Fleet use were also made at Hartfield. A Torpedo/Spotter/Reconnaisance biplane, it was typical of a whole generation of Blackburn aircraft which had served the Royal Navy ever since carriers had been introduced in 1918. It was designed in 1933 and first flew in the following year. The Mark III differed from its predecessors in that it had covered canopy over the cockpit, and incorporated various other improvements.

The Shark was constructed from metal and, with the exception of the wings which were covered with fabric and doped, clad with Alclad sheet aluminium. In service use with the Royal Navy, it was a popular aircraft with a reputation for sturdiness. Sadly, it lost out to its contemporary and rival, the Fairey Swordfish. Both were designed about the same time and some swear that the reason the Shark was dropped in favour of the Swordfish was simply because it used Alclad sheet which at that time was required for use in the new high speed fighters and other machines.

Many of the Dumbarton workers were aircraft buffs and quickly realised that the Shark was an obsolescent machine in comparison with the modern aluminium clad monoplanes, already about to enter service use. Not surprisingly, workers were disappointed not to have the opportunity to build a more modern fighting machine, although in actual fact, training on the Shark stood the workforce in good stead for their later work on the fabric-covered Fairey Swordfish, components for which were produced at the factory from 1940 until 1944. The Blackburn version of the Swordfish was usually referred to as the Blackfish.

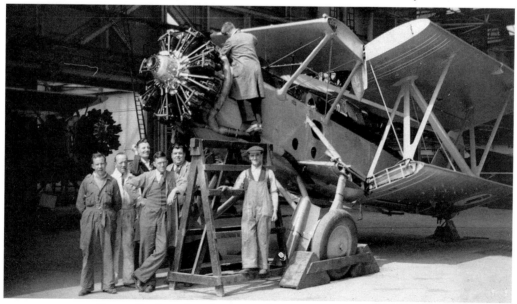

Fergus Steele and workmates in frontof Blackburn Shark, 1938.
Photograph reproduced by permission of Fergus Steele.

The Blackburn B20

If you had visited the Blackburn factory for a tour in the early forties, one of the first things you would have noticed was the pointed way in which your guide carefully avoided taking you anywhere near the final assembly shop. If you were curious and asked him, he (and in the forties, it was always a he) would either say that he didn't know, or murmur quietly to you that the work was secret. In the days of war-time, it was considered patriotic to observe a veil of secrecy. One wonders what today's investigative journalists would have thought.

So what dark secret was hidden in the Final Assembly shop? Owners of the 200,000 £1 shares in the newly formed Blackburn Aircraft Company of Brough were invited to the first AGM at Brough 4 July 1936. At that meeting, the Chairman and Managing Director, Mr Robert Blackburn, revealed that the company shortly anticipated receiving an order to build a new and revolutionary flying boat. This was the work of the company's Chief Seaplane Designer, Major J.D. Rennie, who had already patented the principle of making the bottom planing surface of a flying boat retractable into the main hull using hydraulic jacks. Alastair W. Crichton, a junior draughtsman in the B20 design team in 1940 explains:

> The main difficulty of flying boat design is to arrange that the airscrews clear the water when taxiing, whilst creating a clean aerodynamic shape once the machine is in the air. The B20 was designed to solve these problems. Once the machine took off with the main hull separated from the planing surface, it looked for all the world just like a large seaplane with floats. When airborne, the powerful hydraulic jacks pulled the planing surface up to join the main hull making the machine a normal flying boat.

The boat had been designed in response to Air Ministry specification R1/36, and although Blackburn did not win the contract, which was awarded to Saunders-Roe for their Lerwick Flying Boat, the Ministry was sufficiently interested in Major Rennie's novel design to commission the construction of a prototype. At the time, the project was designated 'most secret' and work on the B20 was not publicly revealed until an article appeared in the 22 June 1945 issue of the *Aeroplane* magazine some nine years later.

Opposite: Blackburn B20 on the Clyde, April 1940. *Photograph reproduced by permission of British Aerospace (Defence) Ltd (Brough Heritage Group).*

With a wingspan of only 82 feet, the B20 was not large by flying boat standards (C-Class Empire Flying Boats of the same period had a 112 feet span). However, in addition to the experimental new hull, the machine was also to pioneer a new and powerful aircraft engine, the 24 cylinder, liquid cooled, supercharged, 1720 hp Rolls Royce Vulture. This advanced engine had been designed to power a whole string of aircraft still on the drawing board. Unfortunately, according to Bill Gunston, author of *Rolls Royce Aero Engines* (Patrick Stephens Ltd), it had a number of major design faults. These, coupled with the difficulty, or as Bill calls it, 'the irritation' of access to its 48 spark plugs and 96 valves, caused production to be abandoned at 538 engines.

The B20 was intended to operate with a crew of eight or nine, and was expected to have a cruising speed of 200 mph with a range of 1,500 miles. According to the company's records and Air Ministry flight test reports, performance was well up to expectations, with the experimental retractable planing bottom operating successfully and completely justifying the designer's claims. However, the personal report of Freddy Weeks (one of the two survivors of the B20's aircrew) is not quite so optimistic. During flight tests in March and April 1940, the aircraft was damaged by birds and was repaired at the factory, as Fergus Steele recalls:

> Together with another chap, I had to knock out the damaged panels and replace them in time for fresh flight trials. We did the job quickly and efficiently and I remember the Inspector being full of praise about our work. In retrospect, I wish that we had delayed the job, or found some excuse to delay the tests, for it was only a few days later that I heard that the aircraft, being flown by the Company's Chief Test Pilot, Flight Lieutenant H. Bailey, crashed.

The Air Ministry Flying Accident Record Card reads as follows:

> Flight Lieutenant H. Bailey was test flying the Blackburn B20 on 7 April 1940 when the machine went out of control and crashed into the sea off Garroch Head. Two crew members baled out safely, but Flt Lt Bailey baled out too late and was killed. Two other crew members are listed as missing.

According to Air Ministry records, all members of the crew were Blackburn employees. In spite of the relative success of the aircraft, it was decided not to proceed with further production. At that stage of the war, the Battle of the Atlantic was just getting into full swing and Blackburn, at the request of the Air Ministry, was committed in principle to quantity production of the Short Sunderland Flying Boat, under licence from designers Short Brothers.

The staff involved in designing the machine felt devastated, none more so than Ken McGregor, who joined the company as an apprentice draughtsman in 1937 and worked on the secret project:

> When I first met the Englishman who became my brother-in law, he told me that his mother's cousin was a man called Bailey, who had been a test pilot with Blackburn. I got quite a shock and I said, 'I'm afraid that I killed him.'

Before I spoke to Richard Weeks, I had come to the conclusion that the story of the B20 had been lost for ever. However, after speaking to him I realised that his father, Frederick Weeks, had indeed recorded his memories. Almost twenty years after the war was over, Freddy decided to put his memories of the crash down on paper, prompted by the interest of a local journalist, Joe King of the *Hull Daily Mail*. This first article was followed by a more technical one in 1974, published in *Aircraft Illustrated*, featuring both survivors of the crash and written by Derek N. James. Richard Weeks, together with the editors of these journals, have kindly given permission for the following extract to be published:

> On Sunday 7 April 1940, five of us were detailed for the fifth test flight of the B20. Originally only four had been scheduled to make up the crew but almost at the last minute we were joined by Ivan Waller, the Rolls Royce engine specialist. The first four fairly short flights had gone relatively smoothly, although the retractable planing bottom had been much slower to retract than in tests on the ground. The wind resistance seemed to make it move up in fits and starts. The minor bird

Flt/Lt Harry Bailey, Blackburn's Chief Test Pilot, seen entering a Blackburn Skua, 1937. *Photograph reproduced by permission of Flight International.*

damage, which had been sustained on the fourth flight, had also been repaired. Our 'skipper' was Flight Lieutenant Harry Bailey, the Company's Chief Test Pilot and apart from Ivan Waller and myself, the crew consisted of two other local Blackburn staff who were monitoring the test equipment for both airframe and engines. Their names were Duncan Robertson and Sam McMillan. I had worked with them on the B20 project for some time and they were two very nice friendly chaps. The brief given to the captain was to fly at 6,000 feet and carry out a programme of engine tests at speeds ranging from around 125 mph to the maximum, with the retractable planing bottom both retracted and lowered. Harry Bailey was, of course, in the left-hand seat flying the machine while I was in the right-hand seat monitoring the engine operation. Ivan Waller was standing in the flight engineer's position between the two of us.

Towards the end of our programme Flt Lt Bailey warned us that he intended to do a maximum speed run with the planing bottom fully retracted into the fuselage. We had only been travelling at the maximum speed for about a couple of minutes when the B20 began to shudder almost out of control. The Captain shouted to close the throttle and Ivan did so, but instead of helping, it made the vibration much worse. After a short while, the skipper gave the order to abandon aircraft. We were all wearing what were called observer-type parachutes which meant that we had a reinforced canvas harness fitted to our body, with hooks fitted to hold the chute, but the actual parachutes were stored further aft. The captain tried to keep the aircraft flying while Ivan Waller and I raced for the chutes. I was just a bit behind him and I was racing back with two chutes, one for the captain, the other for me when I was thrown across the cabin as the machine lurched. I got stuck under the chart table but eventually managed to clip on my own chute as well as the skipper's and open the second escape hatch above his head. The other hatch was already open as, by this time, Ivan had baled out. As I exited the machine, I was surprised to see that his parachute had snagged on the wireless aerial and I could see that he was frantically tearing at it to disentangle it. I tumbled down the aircraft bumping against the tailplane but, all of a sudden, the world was silent and I was floating down on my own. I looked up at the stricken machine and Ivan was still attempting to free himself from the aerial. Eventually he got free (without finger nails), but at least he got out. I saw the plane go down in a spiral but only one chute came out, just before it hit the water.

I found out later that Harry had managed to bale out, but he left it too late and his parachute did not open. It was very typical of his generous nature that he should sacrifice his own life for those of his comrades. Sadly too, both Duncan and Sam did not get out and, as far as I know, their bodies were never found. They were both excellent tradesmen and fine men too. By then I was almost in the drink and a few feet before I hit the water I released my chute. The brisk wind at sea level whipped it away from me at great rate of knots. It was bitterly cold in the water and although I can't really remember the exact time, I think that I was floating in my 'mae west' (life jacket) for about an hour before the Armed Merchant Cruiser *Transylvania* came along and rescued me. To begin with the crew of the lifeboat rowed toward the parachute, but, of course I was miles away from where I was coughing and spluttering in the freezing water. They finally pulled me aboard and we made for Glasgow. I entered the B20 as a civilian and arrived in Glasgow, dressed as a sailor. After the incident, I stayed with Blackburn until 1942, when I joined the Air Transport Auxiliary and flew for the remainder of the war as a First Officer Flight Engineer.

After the war Freddy, as he was always known in Dumbarton, set up his own engineering company and worked as its Managing Director until he died in 1979.

Blackburn B26 Botha

In 1935, the Air Ministry issued a specification for a twin-engined short/medium range bomber which was capable of having a torpedo stowed internally. Two companies responded with designs, namely the Bristol Beaufort and Blackburn Botha. Both machines planned to use the same engine, the Bristol Perseus. The specification was for a three seat aeroplane, but at the last minute the Ministry decided that operational requirements called for four seats and the design was hastily amended.

It quickly became apparent that the redesigned model required a more powerful engine. As Bristol had already allocated all available supplies of the more powerful Taurus engine to their own design, the Beaufort, none were available for the Botha. Blackburn submitted a proposal for a Botha II using another more powerful Bristol engine, but this was turned down by the Ministry as they already had other plans for the use of this engine.

Orders for the Botha were nonetheless placed in December 1936, and detail design and tooling work commenced early in 1937. Production did

The last of the Bothas on the production line, 22 March 1941. *Photograph reproduced by permission of British Aerospace (Defence) Ltd (Brough Heritage Group).*

Botha on the ground at Brough, March 1940. *Photograph reproduced by permission of British Aerospace (Defence) Ltd (Brough Heritage Group).*

not begin until the factory opened at Dumbarton around August 1938, and the first machine, L6347, was delivered in late October 1939. Only one squadron—No. 608 (North Riding) with Coastal Command—used the Botha operationally, and no Dumbarton machines took part in this limited experiment. The squadron also flew the Avro Anson, a much older, slower and more vulnerable aircraft. However, while the Ansons had regular contact with enemy aircraft and U-Boats, the Bothas were out of luck and spent hundreds of uneventful hours patrolling over the North Sea. They were subsequently withdrawn from service and passed to OTUs, wireless and gunner schools and other training units, where they performed a useful role until 1943 when they were scrapped. The Dumbarton factory produced 200 machines in about 17 months and the total production by both Brough and Dumbarton was 580. Once the Botha had reached the training units and the operational squadron, reports began to filter back to the factory about the cramped fuselage conditions, the weak undercarriage and the uncertain one-engine performance, and workers were not too surprised by the cancellation of orders for the aircraft.

The Short Sunderland

Early in 1940, It became clear that the U-Boat was going to be the German's main weapon of war, and at that time few aircraft had either sufficient range or bomb load-capacity to protect convoys crossing the Atlantic. The sole British exception was the Short Sunderland, and in consequence it was decided to step up production so that our convoys, particularly those in the Atlantic, would have adequate protection.

The Sunderland was developed from the Short C Class Empire Flying Boat, which had already proved extremely reliable in long journeys to the far-flung outposts of the British Empire. Because of its large load-capacity it was an excellent vehicle for carrying depth charges, and was much feared by the Germans. They nicknamed it *Fliegende Stachelschwein* (The Flying Porcupine), because of its formidable defensive fire power. In view of these qualities, the Air Ministry decided to expand production of the Sunderland, which was being produced at the Short factory in Rochester, Kent, at the time. However, because of the ever-increasing threat of air

Work in progress on Short Sunderlands at Dumbarton, 1942. *Photograph reproduced by permission of British Aerospace (Defence) Ltd (Brough Heritage Group).*

Fairey Swordfish (Blackfish), 1942. *Photograph reproduced by permission of British Aerospace (Defence) Ltd (Brough Heritage Group).*

raids, plus the possibility of invasion, it was decided to disperse production throughout the country to Shorts in Belfast and Windermere, and to Blackburn in Dumbarton.

The choice of the Blackburn factory was an understandable one; not only were the facilities appropriate, but a proportion of the workforce and all of the management were experienced in flying boat production. Initially, the Dumbarton factory was given the contract to build 15 Mk1 Sunderlands, but it is a tribute to the newly learned skills of the Scottish workforce and the long standing 'Clyde Built' tradition that this order was quickly increased, with the factory finally completing 250 Sunderlands by October 1945. This was no mean feat. The Sunderland was 85 feet long with a wingspan of 112 feet and as high as a three storey tenement building. It was also crammed with radio and electronic gear, and the production of 250 in five years averages out at almost one of these gigantic machines per week.

Sunderlands were not only impressive, they were also very tough. The first of the aircraft constructed at the Dumbarton factory, T9083, was completed in October 1940 and launched just prior to the required delivery date of 26 October. It enjoyed a comparatively tranquil life. On the other hand the next machine, T9084, had a quite different history. After acceptance by the RAF it was allocated to No. 228 Squadron. During the withdrawal from Greece in 1941, the squadron's Sunderlands were deployed to evacuate as many RAF and Army technicians as possible. The story is recorded in Chaz Bowyer's excellent book on the Sunderland:

Flt/Lt Harry Lamont skippering T9084 . . . In the afternoon I was sent to Kalamata, where a whole host of army and a few RAF were assembling on what was the last bit of Greece they could get to. I didn't have all that much fuel on board and calculated that we would be all right with 80 and took on that number (I believe that they were counted off as 82!) That made 92 on board with the crew. But it was no trouble for T9084 and she took off like a bird.

We arranged them (the passengers) from the front turret to the end of the step and she balanced out almost dead right. I was being re-fuelled for an op the next day when the re-fuelling was stopped and I was ordered off for the third time that day to do a night trip to Kalamata—without a flare path either end. I had to take a message; about Navy plans to mount an evacuation exercise, I believe, though I was not told that. The take-off was hair-raising as there were plenty of sunken ships in Suda Bay with bits above water, but it was dark and misty and much too calm at Kalamata for landing using only the landing lights We had some trouble finding our way there, but I didn't have enough fuel to hang around for daylight and I couldn't land back at Suda, so land at Kalamata it had to be. I never saw the surface—and poor old T9084 tore out her nose plates and turned over.

Fortunately all members of the crew survived the crash, although one was injured and all had to spend four years in Germany as Prisoners of War.

Fairey Swordfish (Blackfish)

The full records of the Dumbarton Factory are no longer available, but various items of evidence support the view that Swordfish components were produced at the Dumbarton plant. The main contract for the machine was placed at the Sherburn-in-Elmet Blackburn factory, following the Air Ministry's decision to withdraw the work from Fairey Aviation's own works to allow them space to produce other machines. However, workers at Dumbarton claim to have taken part in production of Swordfish wings and tail surfaces from 1940 until 1944. I have been shown numerous pieces of Swordfish which were 'souvenired', and which substantiate this, along with a letter from Brough addressed to the Dumbarton plant, congratulating the staff on achieving production targets.

Ernest Dickens

After extensive enquiries to track down any surviving members of the Dumbarton factory management, I made contact with Mrs Barbara Barnes, daughter of the late Ernie Dickens. Although her father was no longer alive, she was able to put me in touch with Mr Richard Weeks (the son of Freddie Weeks, one of the survivors of the B20 accident). Mrs Barnes was also able to provide information about her late father's role in the factory, as well as photographs and documents telling the story of his visit to Cyprus, the Somaliland Protectorate and Ethiopia to supervise the erection of Shipston Buildings in 1959-60. This related to the use of pre-fabricated housing manufactured at Dumbarton, and the story of Ernie's trip gives an insight into the dramatic changes which have taken place in air travel in the last thirty-five or so years.

At the request of the Diplomatic Wireless service, I visited Limassol, Cyprus to clear up the final erection of a canteen. The trip was uneventful apart from a bus ride to Nicosia—the bus was full of natives with their poultry and goats, etc.

My next duty was to supervise the erection of seven type 72 houses, one type 75 villa for H.I.W. Haile Sellassie and three schools spread out at different sites in the Ogaden desert. On the same tour I had to supervise the erection of seven houses for the Diplomatic Wireless service in Berbera, Somaliland.

The flight from Renfrew to Addis Ababa via London, Frankfurt, Athens, Cairo and Asmara took twenty-five hours. The flight between Frankfurt and Athens was very rough, with seat belt fastened all the way.

The Ministry of Public Works arranged for me to fly out to Gabredarre in a military Dakota. This was very uncomfortable as the centre of the aircraft was piled up with petrol, paraffin, and all kinds of supplies required on these outposts, leaving only a tin seat at the side for passengers. It was terribly hot inside, with no drinking water or a chance to stretch your legs for four hours.

The contractor was Italian and could not speak English, but we eventually got a team of natives, marked out the site, sorted out the components and sub-assembled as much as possible while the foundations were being prepared. The erection of the villa was

well under way and the contractor had a good idea of the system before I left to start off the erection in Berbera.

I arrived at Berbera via Dire Dawa, Addis, Djibouti and Aden on a Saturday afternoon, with no contact, checked in at the Rest House (a bed and concrete bath) the only guest, with two Somali boys to look after the place. I contacted the Public Works Department on Monday morning and we made a start the following day.

The labour here was entirely native with no engineering knowledge whatever. I saw more screws put in cross thread in six weeks than I have seen in my whole life.

Ernest Dickens (left) outside a Shipston building, Ethopia.

We had erected the structure of the seven houses and completed the first, when I received a cable to return to Ethiopia. No seat was available on the plane, so I worked my passage across to Aden on an RAF Z craft.

We sailed for Berbera 6 p.m. 20th January 1960. The steering jammed about thirty miles out and we went around in circles until we rectified the trouble. An hour later one engine broke down, so we finished the trip doing three knots, arriving at Aden the following night about 10.30 p.m.

It took just three days in Aden to get my re-entry visa for Ethiopia. On arrival in Addis I was informed by the Ministry of Public Works that the six houses for Gabredarre had been re-allocated to different sites about 300 miles apart, and this would mean doing the tour by Land Rover.

I flew into Dire Dawa and met the Engineer in charge of the Ogaden project (Abdul Samed). We loaded petrol, food and water and started the tour. Our first site was Jig Jiga and the roads were very rough, the route being mostly around and over mountains. We arrived late in the evening and got accommodation in a loft.

During our stay there we met the German contractors building schools and hospitals. They had caravans with all the latest equipment, including radio telephone, but they greatly admired the Shipston construction; they even admitted it was much better then their method in all ways.

When we were satisfied that the team were able to finish the house, we continued our journey to the next site, Aware. The roads were very rough—a mixture of sand and rocks—and we had to camp the night in a police enclosure about half way, and set off at dawn the next day.

We arrived at Aware before dark and set up camp in a hut loaned to us by the Governor.

The site was marked out and a team with one Italian was started off on erection.

Our next site was Gabredarre to continue the erection of the

Order comes fom chaos at the Gabredarre site.

villa and one house. I set off with the engineer and a native driver at 5.30 a.m., but we failed to pick up the tracks in the dark. The engineer and the driver quarrelled and we returned to camp where the driver was later arrested for sabotaging the Land Rover.

During this delay I watched the distribution of Milo grain (gifted by the people of the USA) to the natives. They were identified by their chief as they passed down the line. The sacks were given to the women to carry—the men just walked alongside.

We eventually set off again for Gabredarre where we arrived about dusk, dirty and tired having had only biscuits and pineapples to eat all day.

The next two weeks were spent on the finishing operations of the Villa and one house. We shot gazelle on several evenings for fresh meat. The camp here was fairly good with running water, a shower etc., but the insects were a nuisance. There were all kinds of flying insects up to three inches long, and beetles and spiders on the floor as big as your hand.

A new governor was appointed for Gabredarre, and the contractor and I were invited to a banquet. This was a large gathering of all the tribal chiefs in full dress. The meal consisted of scotch whisky and large dishes of raw meat. Needless to say we went back to camp tight but hungry.

We prepared for the trip to the next site at Wardere, but had to wait four days for Gio Campus the contractor to recover from malaria. The roads were just camel tracks, sand and stones as before. We saw many hyenas, a giraffe and ostrich.

We stayed long enough to organise the team for the erection of one house, and visited another two sites before packing food and water for the final trip to Dole on the border of Kenya, about 700 miles away.

We covered about 150 miles the first day, but had much trouble with tyres—seven punctures in all. In many places bridges were missing.

The first night was spent on the floor in a military outpost.

After filling up with water at a water hole near the camp, an early start was made the next morning, but only to get lost in the bush with lions brushing past the Land Rover. We eventually found the track with the help of a native boy (Ali).

Nearing Dole two days later, we arrived late at night on the wrong side of the river (Ganale Doria). We camped on the river side for three days before we found a place to cross.

Steps had to be cut in the bank to get the Land Rover down to the river bed, and natives spread out to wade across and indicate the deep channels. Our engine stalled in mid stream, and many more natives had to be recruited to push us out.

A camp was set up on site consisting of a few roof sheets with sand bags to keep them from being blown away. Ten days were spent there, checking material and organising the team.

I awoke one night to see our next dinner, the leg of a gazelle, disappearing into the bush.

The journey back to Addis Ababa took three days. The first 400 miles were over rough country with hardly any roads, and we had many steep climbs and descents.

We covered the last 300 miles in one day on very good roads through lovely green country and many lakes.

Returned to Dumbarton	Saturday 27 February, 1960.
Total flying time	120 hours.
Land Rover approx.	3,000 miles.

Barney Coleman with the maintenance team, 1948. *Photograph reproduced by permission of Barney Coleman.*

Products manufactured by the Dumbarton factory as orders for aircraft declined included trailers such as this one. *Photograph reproduced by permission of Alastair W. Crichton.*

Sharks being completed at the new factory, September 1937. *Photograph reproduced by permission of British Aerospace (Defence) Ltd (Brough Heritage Group).*

Some of the contributors to this book:
Back row: Fergus Steele, Hugh Galloway, Ken McGregor, Barney Coleman, Alistair Crichton, Malcolm Wallace.
Front row: Mary McGinlay, Barbara Wright, Barbara Barnes, Margaret Bashford, Grace Kennedy.
Photograph reproduced by permission of Frank Smith of the Dumbarton Camera Club.